Mr Big was a giant.

He was a very, very big giant.

He lived in a big house with big windows and

a big door.

One day it was Mr Big's birthday.

Some children came to Mr Big's house.

They were carrying a big yellow jelly.

The children said, 'We have made

a jelly for you, but is it too big?'

'No problem,' said Mr Big,

3

Some children came into Mr Big's garden.

They were carrying a big sandwich.

They said, 'We have made a sandwich for you, but is it too big?'

'No problem,' said Mr Big,

5

Some children had made a gingerbread man for Mr Big.

They said, 'We have made a big gingerbread man for you, but is it too big?'

'No problem,' said Mr Big,

Mr Big had a surprise for the children.
He said, 'I have made a giant cake for
you, but is it too big?'
The children laughed and said, 'No problem.
We can eat it.'